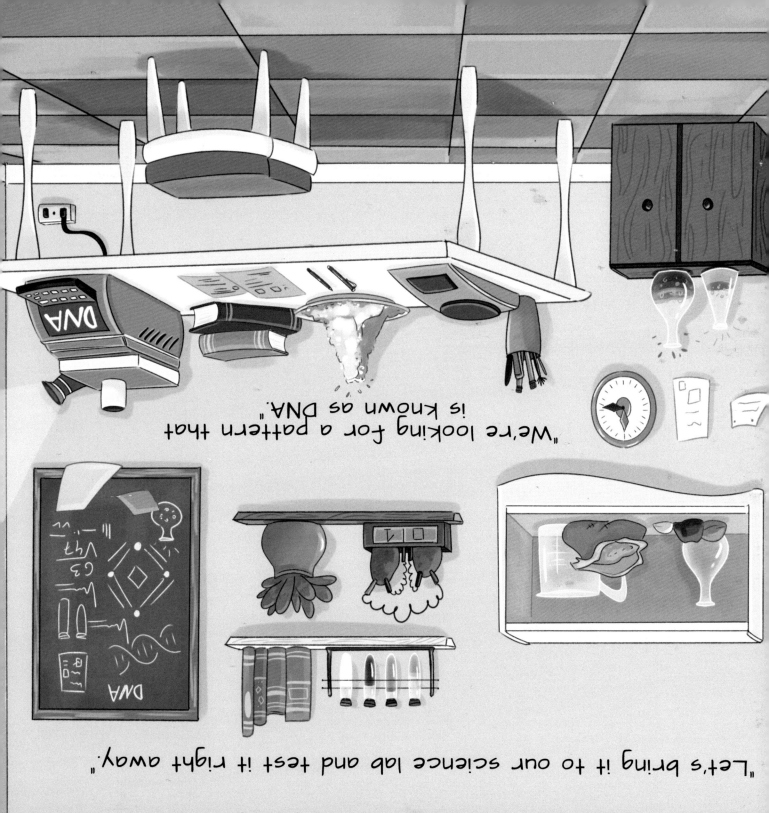

"We're looking for a pattern that is known as DNA."

"Let's bring it to our science lab and test it right away."

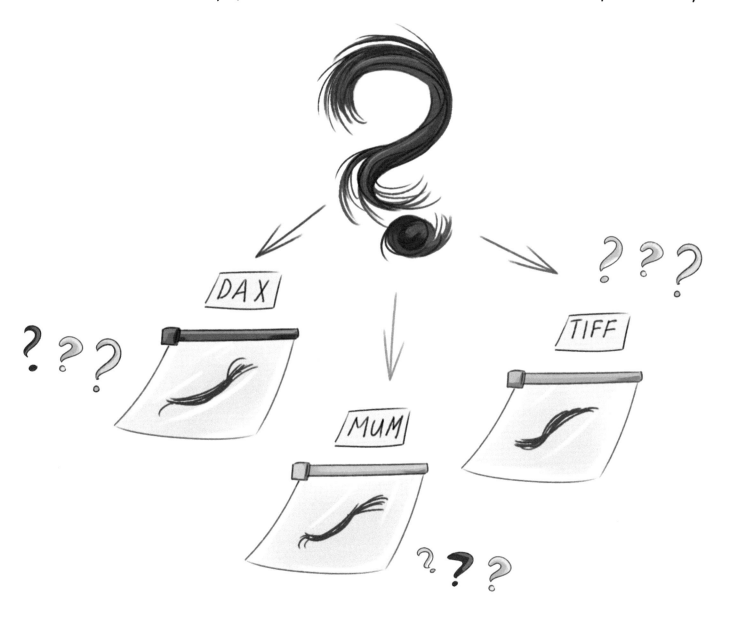

The Missiny Birthday Cake

A DNA Science Mystery

with the
Dinky Amigos
and
YOU

First Published in Great Britain 2021
by Dinky Press Ltd

ISBN 978-1-914581-00-7

Text Copyright © Lisa Mullan 2021
Illustration Copyright © Indira Muzbulakova (Beehive Illustrations) 2021

British Library Cataloguing-in-Publication Data
A catalogue record for this book is available from the British Library

https://www.dinkyamigos.com

This book belongs to:

_____

For Grace's birthday tea, her mum had promised she would bake,

She ran in through the kitchen door and saw ...

A

sticky,

spongey,

yummy,

gooey,

creamy,

rainbow cake.

So after school, Grace hurtled home and skidded past the gate

"Whoever ate my cake," said Grace, "they didn't even share."

"To find out who," the sergeant said,

"we need to test the hair."

Perhaps the hair was from her dog, a tiny pug called Dax.

Did he mistake her birthday treat for tasty doggy snacks?

As Grace looked all around the room, she spotted Tiff the cat.

Her cute and fluffy tortoiseshell has fur that looks like that.

Mum's hair is short like that one and exactly the same shade!

But would she take and eat the cake surprise that she'd just made?

"Aha!"

he cried aloud, "I think this hair could be our clue."

A strand that's brown and kind of short...

A strand of hair from

who?

Her rainbow cake had vanished and now only crumbs were left.

She needed a policeman to report a birthday theft.

A sergeant came to help and he confirmed the plate was bare.

But poking out beneath that plate, a strand of

short, brown hair.

But DNA is tiny and its pattern barely shows.

Dinky Amigos

Tristan

Alina

Crispin

Gina

We need our little friends to help,
the Dinky Amigos.

Each hair will have a pattern that is different, not the same.

If we can match the patterns up, we'll all know who's to blame.

To solve this hairy problem, Grace will need some help from you.

Can you work out which row agrees exactly with our clue?

The hair we found will be the first to undergo this test.

The pattern for our strand is back. We need to check the rest.

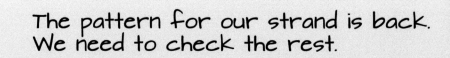

A hair from Grace's mum is now
the second to be done.

Do these two Dinky patterns
match and pair up one by one?

Up next, we'll test a furry strand from Grace's feline friend.

Does this new pattern look the same and match from end to end?

Just one more pattern left and only one more match to make.

Could Dax have been the one to eat the missing birthday cake?

You're right - it was the dog! And now you've helped Grace find the cheat.

Her greedy pet had wolfed the cake and spoiled her teatime treat.

She smiled and thanked the sergeant, "You are such a super sleuth!"

And Grace says, "Thanks!" to you as well for helping find the truth.

Can you solve these mini-mysteries?

Which colours were on the cake?

Where was the hair?

Who did Grace phone?

How many books on the bookshelf?

Who ate the birthday cake?

The DNA Science Mystery Club

with the
Dinky Amigos
and
YOU

Want more mysteries, puzzles, games and codes with a DNA theme?

Join the DNA Science Mystery Club on behalf of your child and grab their Sleuth Starter Pack now.

sleuth.dinkyamigos.com/starterpack